Im Supern
At the Supermarket

Susanne Böse

Sigrid Leberer

Edition bi:libri

Marie freut sich, denn heute geht sie mit Mama einkaufen. Marie kennt sich schon gut aus im Supermarkt. Zuerst holt sie einen Einkaufswagen. Es gibt auch Einkaufskörbe zum Tragen, doch so einer ist heute zu klein.

Mary is excited because she gets to go shopping with her mom. Mary already knows her way around the supermarket. First she gets a shopping cart. There are shopping baskets you can carry, but one of those would be too small today.

der Einkaufswagen

shopping cart

der Einkaufskorb

shopping basket

die Torte

cake

der Kuchen

cake

Gleich am Eingang ist der Bäcker. Es duftet köstlich nach Kuchen und frischem Brot. Mama kauft Brötchen, ein Vollkornbrot und eine Torte. Heute kommt Besuch! Außerdem bekommt Marie eine knusprige Brezel.

The bakery is right at the front of the store. The cake and fresh bread smell great. Mom buys rolls, whole grain bread and a cake. Guests are coming today! Mary also gets a fresh, crispy pretzel.

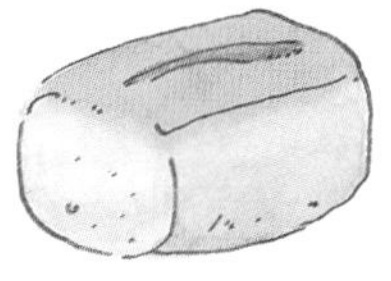

das Weißbrot

white bread

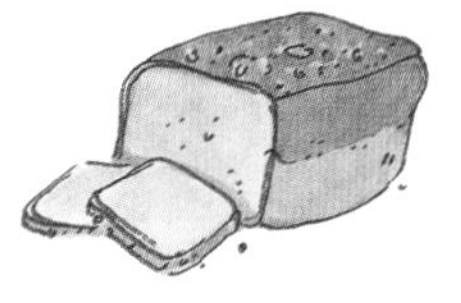

das Vollkornbrot

whole grain bread

das Brötchen

roll

die Brezel

pretzel

Wie lecker das Obst aussieht! Marie legt Äpfel, Bananen und Orangen in den Einkaufswagen. Außerdem duftende Pfirsiche und Zitronen. Ob sie auch Erdbeeren, Aprikosen und Kiwis nehmen darf? Oder die Ananas da? Oder Weintrauben? Mama schüttelt schon den Kopf.
Da hat Marie eine Idee: „Wir können doch einen Obstsalat machen. Du sagst ja immer, Vitamine sind wichtig.“ Mama lacht und legt noch eine Wassermelone dazu.

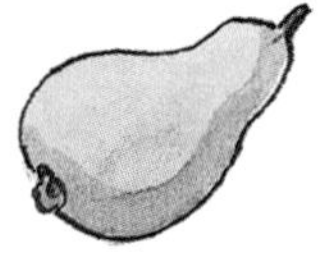			
die Birne	der Pfirsich	die Erdbeere	die Pflaume
pear	**peach**	**strawberry**	**plum**

The fruit looks so good! Mary puts apples, bananas and oranges into the shopping cart and then adds sweet-smelling peaches and lemons. Can she take strawberries, apricots and kiwis, too? Or the pineapple over there? Or grapes? Mom shakes her head.
Mary has an idea: "We could make a fruit salad. You always say vitamins are important." Mom laughs and puts a watermelon in the cart.

die Zitrone
lemon

die Wassermelone
watermelon

die Weintrauben (pl.)
grapes

die Kirschen (pl.)
cherries

Jetzt kommt das Gemüse dran. Mama sieht auf dem Einkaufszettel nach: Sie brauchen Kopfsalat, eine Gurke, Tomaten, Paprika, eine Aubergine, Zwiebeln, Kartoffeln, Petersilie und Basilikum.

The vegetables are next. Mom checks her shopping list: they need lettuce, a cucumber, tomatoes, bell peppers, an eggplant, onions, potatoes, parsley and basil.

der Kopfsalat	der Knoblauch	die Karotte	die Aubergine
lettuce	garlic	carrot	eggplant

Doch wo stehen denn bloß die Kräuter? Kannst du sie finden?
Und was für ein Gemüse isst du am liebsten?

Where are the herbs? Can you find them? And what kind of vegetable do you like best?

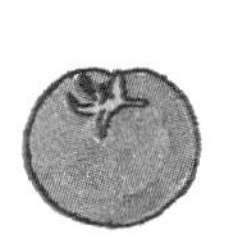
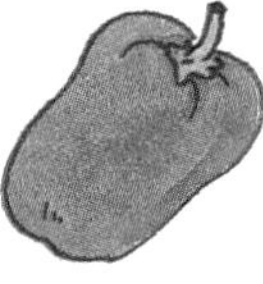

die Tomate	die Paprika	die Gurke	die Kartoffel	die Zwiebel
tomato	bell pepper	cucumber	potato	onion

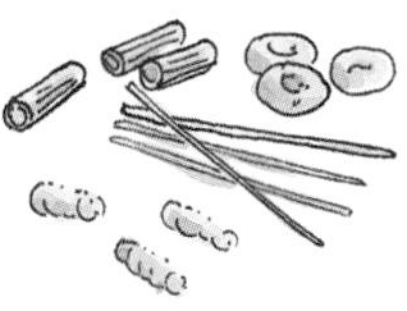

die Nudeln (pl.)

noodles

der Reis

rice

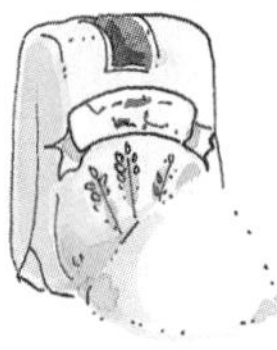

das Mehl

flour

der Zucker

sugar

„Kaffee, Tee und Kakao sind im Sonderangebot“, murmelt Mama.
Der Einkaufswagen wird immer voller: Mehl, Zucker und Salz, Nudeln, Spaghetti und Reis ... „Wo ist das Müsli?“, fragt Marie. Mama zeigt es ihr.

“Coffee, tea and cocoa are on sale,” murmurs Mom.
The shopping cart is getting fuller and fuller: flour, sugar and salt, noodles, spaghetti and rice… “Where is the cereal?” asks Mary. Mom shows her.

das Salz/der Pfeffer

salt/pepper

der Kakao

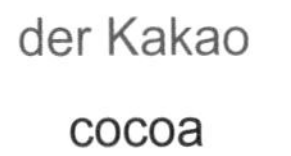

cocoa

der Tee

tea

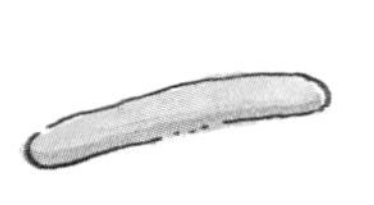

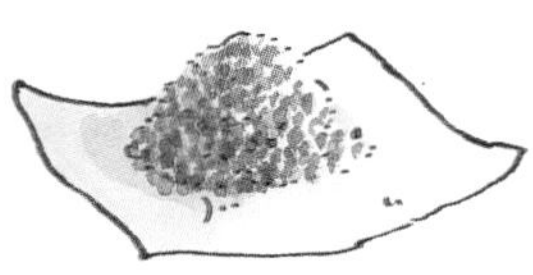

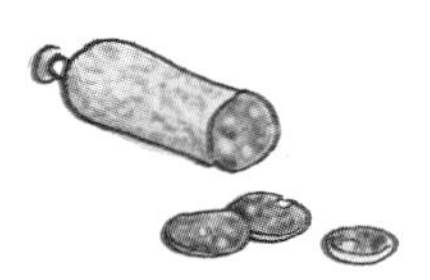

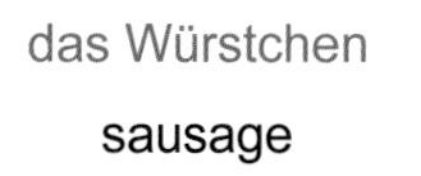

das Würstchen	das Hackfleisch	das Hühnchen	die Salami
sausage	**ground meat**	**chicken**	**salami**

Der Metzger hat köstliche Dinge im Angebot: Würstchen, Salami oder Schinken mag Marie sehr. Doch noch lieber isst sie Hühnchen oder ein saftiges Steak. Gut, dass Papa so gerne grillt!
Danach bestaunt Marie die Fischtheke. „Mama, guck mal!“, ruft sie aufgeregt und zeigt auf einen großen Fisch. Der sieht ja wirklich komisch aus. Mama lacht und nimmt von der Verkäuferin den Lachs entgegen.

The butcher has lots of delicious things to offer: Mary really likes sausages, salami and ham. But she likes chicken or a juicy steak even more. It’s a good thing that Dad loves to barbeque!
Mary stares at the fish counter in amazement. “Mom, look!” she cries out excitedly and points to a big fish. It looks really funny. Mom laughs and takes some salmon from the saleswoman.

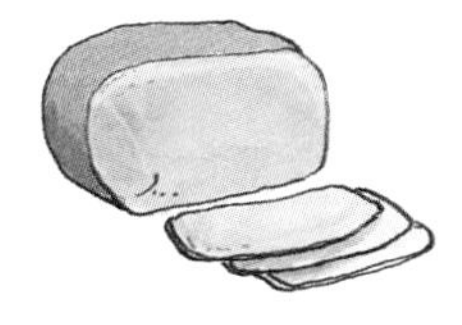
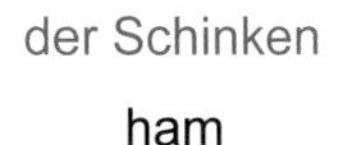

der Schinken
ham

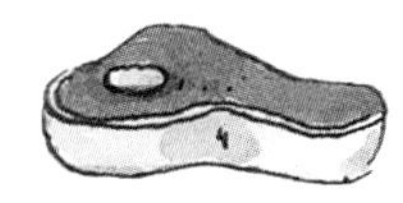

das Steak
steak

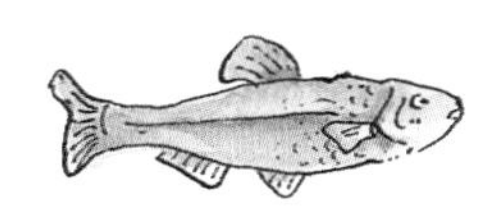

der Fisch
fish

die Garnele
shrimp

„Jetzt noch Käse", murmelt Mama mit Blick auf ihren Einkaufszettel.
Sie kaufen Mozzarella, Schafskäse, Ziegenkäse, Frischkäse und Parmesan.
Der Verkäufer gibt Marie ein Stück zum Naschen.

"Now for the cheese," Mom murmurs with a glance at her shopping list.
They buy mozzarella, sheep cheese, goat cheese, cream cheese and parmesan.
The salesperson gives Mary a piece to nibble on.

der Käse
cheese

die Sahne
cream

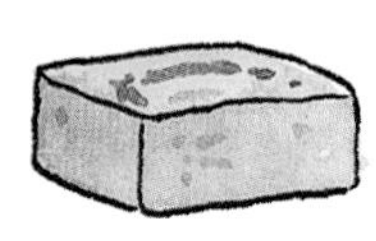

die Butter
butter

der Pudding
pudding

Während Mama noch Oliven aussucht, geht Marie zum Kühlregal weiter. Milch, Butter und Sahne interessieren sie ja nicht so sehr. Dafür mag sie Joghurt und Pudding umso mehr. Welchen soll Marie nehmen? Vanille oder Schoko?

While Mom picks out olives, Mary continues on to the dairy coolers. She's not too interested in the milk, butter or cream. But she likes yogurt and pudding a lot. Which should Mary take? Vanilla or chocolate?

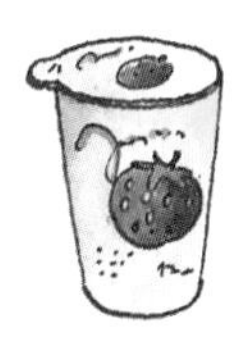

der Fruchtjoghurt

fruit yogurt

die Milch

milk

die Oliven (pl.)

olives

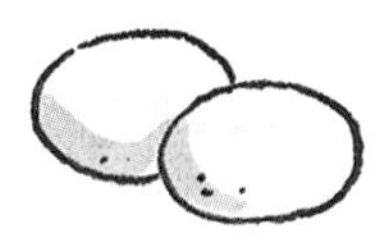

das Ei

egg

das Öl

oil

der Essig

vinegar

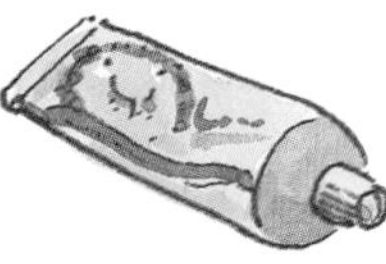

der Senf

mustard

die Marmelade

jam

Uff. Geschafft! Zuhause packen sie alles aus. Mama fängt schon mal an zu kochen. „Was gibt's denn?", fragt Papa neugierig. „Spaghetti mit Tomatensoße", erklärt Marie. „Lecker. Aber musstet ihr dafür den ganzen Supermarkt leer kaufen?" Marie lacht: „Oma und Opa kommen doch!" Mama schaut sich ratlos um. „Sag mal, Marie, wo ist denn das Tomatenmark für die Soße?" Oh nein! Kannst du es dir denken?

Whew. Done! At home, they unpack all the groceries. Mom begins to cook. "What are we having?" asks Dad curiously. "Spaghetti with tomato sauce," says Mary. "Sounds good. But did you have to buy out the whole supermarket for that?" Mary laughs: "Grandma and Grandpa are coming!" Mom looks around confused. "Say, Mary, where is the tomato paste for the sauce?" Oh, no! What do you think happened?

der Honig

honey

der Fruchtsaft

fruit juice

das Wasser

water

die Nüsse (pl.)

nuts

Gemüse

Vegetables

Fleisch und Fisch

Meat and Fish

Getreideprodukte

Grain Products